to do with marital arguments, weight gain, panic attacks, etc?

Probably a hell of a lot mor

What Sleep Is and 1 .... (Nutshell Style)

U.S. Supreme Court Justice Potter Stewart is known, famously, for saying he couldn't define hardcore pornography well, but noted "I know it when I see it." Sleep is generally defined the same way. It's one of those circular definitions we often see, like "the act of sleeping," which drives me bonkers. If you have read anything else I have written ever, you have copped to the fact that I like functional definitions that set the tone for what we're talking about it. So here's one for sleep.

> *Sleep is an active and dynamic cerebral meditative activity that occurs roughly 8 out of every 24 hours, in conjunction with the human circadian rhythm, in which certain areas of the brain are less active and other areas of the brain become more active. This activity affects the function of every major organ*

within the human body, either in positive ways (when this activity is maintained in a healthy manner) or negative ways (when this activity is not maintained in a healthy manner).

When I say *circadian rhythm*, I'm referring to the natural cycle that defines a day for us. Circadian just means "around day," after all. Every species on the planet (barring those that only live a very few days) has a circadian rhythm. It's generated by our internal time clock, but informed by the earth's rotation. For my fellow science nerds, our internal time clock is an actual existing thing in the middle of the brain, called the *suprachiasmatic nucleus.*

Sleep occurs in four different stages that we cycle through during our time asleep. There are three stages of Non-Rapid Eye Movement (NREM) sleep, moving from lighter to heavier, and then there is Rapid Eye Movement (REM) sleep, which is the time period where most of our dreaming occurs.

The cycling through REM and NREM stages is weird AF. There is no symmetry to how it happens, except we do know that the NREM sleep is more dominant early and the REM sleep is more dominant later (and closer to the time we wake up). So if we stay up too late we lose more NREM sleep, and if we have to get up too early we lose more REM sleep. Both are important. Equally so. Let's get on with why that's the case, eh?

Why We Sleep

Science has been historically replete with answering this question with a resounding *"um, not sure…but we know you get fucked-up if you don't."*

Early and Really Dumb Ideas

One early theory was that sleep protected us from predators. The idea was that if we are immobile, we are safer during periods of time when it's riskier to be out and about (nighttime). I mean, OK, you could make an argument for that. You could also make the argument that being awake and alert while bitey, eatey things are on the loose and might be hunting you would make more sense.

Another early theory was one of energy conservation. We use about 10% less energy when we are asleep, which could help us stay alive during times of scarcity. Again, this is a reasonable argument. But so is being awake to go hunt or gather more food sources (energy) to have a net gain to get more stuff done. I mean, we could save 10% of our energy, or we could use it to go hook up a burrito with extra guac and double our energy. Just sayin'.

Understanding why we sleep has actually been one of the final frontiers of how-the-body-works science. And only in recent years do we have a better idea of what's actually going on.

Ensmartening Ourselves

When we are awake we are taking in all kinds of new information, right? NREM and REM sleep have different functions in terms of what our brains do with that information.

The brain is busy during the day, attending to all of our ongoing shenanigans. Sorting through those shenanigans takes time and energy we don't have when we are active. NREM sleep is our time to store this new info, strengthen some connections, and prune away the unnecessary bullshit. It reinforces remembering what we need to remember and forgetting what we need to forget.

REM sleep is the time when we integrate all the info we brought in with the stuff we already knew to be true about the world. REM sleep is essentially our emotional processing time. It helps us recognize patterns and fuels our creativity. This is the likely purpose of the dreaming we do in this stage. It helps us make more intelligent and thoughtful decisions in future days. The brain is figuring out what things are important to remember and what things can be let go of. For those of us working through our old crap and creating new, healthier associations and coping skills, sleep is an important part of all of that happening.

Detoxing our Brains

The latest research shows that essentially sleep time is housekeeping time. Research published by Dr. Maiken Nedergaard in 2013 found that the brain's toxin flushing system (the glymphatic system) is ten times more active when we are asleep than when we are awake. If the brain is a city, the glymphatic system is the brain's sewer system (pleasant image, right?). During sleep our neuroglial cells (the cells that support our neuron functioning; the word "glia" means "glue" in Greek) shrink up, allowing our sewer system to flush out. The toxins are pulled out of the brain and into the bloodstream so the liver and kidneys can process the waste out.

It takes a fuck-ton of energy to propel this process, and the brain doesn't have the energy to spare when it's busy processing information, as it has to during our waking hours. Toxins build up continuously in our brains and bodies as the side effect of being alive on the planet. That's not a cause for concern, as long as the body is equipped to do the cleaning-outing part. For the brain, this process happens continuously as we move through different cycles of sleep.

A Super Weird and Super Interesting Note about Adenosine:

Adenosine is a chemical that exists throughout every cell in the body and is one of the neurotransmitters (chemical messengers) in the brain. Adenosine has an important proactive role in the body—it's a nervous system depressant, meaning it suppresses arousal so we don't have panic attacks 24/7. It builds up during our waking hours and plays a big role in "feeling sleepy." One of the things caffeine does is block the adenosine effect. Adenosine *also* builds up in areas of inflammation. And we are now aware that inflammation occurs from emotional trauma, not just physical trauma, and that neuroinflammation is wayyyy more common than scientists previously realized.

I am first and foremost a trauma therapist. I can't really delve into any topic without seeing how it relates back to human trauma at this point. Every single one of these processes relate to trauma recovery. Dumping old ways of relating to the world and interacting in new and healthy ways? Reducing chronic inflammation and body toxicity? Enhancing decision-making ability and creativity? Hey there my *Unfuck Your Brain* crew…get some sleep!

Are You Getting Enough Sleep?

Don't fucking lie to me, now. You aren't, are you? And you aren't alone. Authors of a National Sleep Foundation report noted that 2/3 of all adults in the U.S. do not get the minimum recommended amount of sleep (seven hours) at least on weeknights, and generally not at all.

And it's not like everyone is coming close but getting 6.5 hours or something. Most people are clocking in way, way less on a regular basis. This isn't just a U.S. problem, however. The 2/3 number is exactly the same in Japan, and nearly that in the UK. Other countries vary in their number count but it's still way, way too high. Even in Germany, where it's "only" 30% of the population who is sleep deprived.

Seven to nine hours: that's what adults are supposed to get. I happen to be a nine-hour person, but seven is the minimum to ward off all the ills I'm going to discuss below. This isn't a Dr. Faith number; this is a World Health Organization number.

"Bah!" a lot of people say. "I'm one of those people who don't need much sleep."

"Bah!" I say in return. Bullshit, alas. The number of people who actually are able to gain all the benefits discussed above on less sleep is minute. Like a fraction of 1%. And it seems to be related to a variant of a specific gene known as BHLHE41.

So why do so many people think they are just fucking fine? Several reasons, I'm guessing.

- The first is the cultural norm of sleep deprivation. We think we are supposed to push through things and be all tough and shit. Sleeping a full seven hours is a cultural sign of weakness.

- We're used to it. We don't realize that this isn't our optimal self. It's just how it's been for so long.

- And finally? Research demonstrates that we greatly underestimate our level of impairment from sleep deprivation. The rate of mistakes we make when sleep deprived has been tested and quantified in studies, but ask us to estimate our level of impairment? We think we've got it under control.

The Effects of Not Enough Quality Sleep

Because sleep is inextricably tied to pretty much every function of the human body, it is thennot a shock that not enough sleep (or disruption of quality sleep) is associated with a multitude of problems. Here's a fun list of things we are far more likely to develop if we are sleep deprived:

- Reduced immune system function and immune deficiency

- Reduced motor function

- Cancer and the spread of cancer

- Diabetes

- Infertility

- Alzheimer's

- Weight gain and obesity

- Depletion of our gut microbiome

- Cardiovascular disease

- High blood pressure

- Higher susceptibility to infections

- Stroke

- Congestive heart failure

- Depression

- Anxiety

- Bipolar disorder

- Schizophrenia

- PTSD

- Suicidality

- Shorter life span

- Vehicle accidents and traffic deaths. Drowsy driving accounts for more accidents and deaths than drugs and alcohol combined.

Now some of these things are causal. Accident rates due to drowsy driving? We make mistakes when impaired. Period. But it isn't always a cause and effect situation. No one is saying (that I'm aware of) that sleep deprivation causes PTSD or any other emotional or physical illness. Correlation is not causality. But treating sleep can greatly reduce the symptoms of these other issues and help promote healing and recovery. A great example? People who were dieting and sleep deprived lost muscle instead of fat. The individuals who were dieting and sleeping lost fat and retained their muscle. Win!

How to Sleep Better

Ok, first of all, if you have the ability to get enough sleep (as in, you can fall asleep just fucking fine) but you don't let yourself get enough sleep (as in, you are binging on Netflix or some dumb shit instead of putting yourself to bed): *stop that shit right now and get enough sleep.* There, easy fix.

Now, for the rest of you who are *trying* to get enough sleep but have trouble doing so and have for some time? Like, you don't sleep well for several nights a week for months on end? Or maybe you're getting crappy sleep quality. Insomnia generally stems from worry, rumination, anxiety, and other types of emotional distress. It's common. One out of nine people meet the criteria for insomnia at any given moment. The rest of this section is for you. Let's unfuck your sleep.

Give Yourself Appropriate Sleep *Opportunity* Time

You need to give yourself a good 30 minutes to fall asleep. So if you need seven hours, put yourself to bed 7.5 hours before wakey-uppy time. Have a regular going to bed and getting up time, even on your days off. I know. The advice "have a bedtime routine" makes you want to throw up in your mouth every time you read it. But have a bedtime routine.

Don't Flop Around Restlessly

If you didn't fall asleep during your 30-minute opportunity window, don't perseverate over it. Don't look at the clock. Don't toss and turn. Get up and go do something. Don't turn on the Xbox or anything super stimulating, and nothing with blue lights in general (read: anything with a screen). Read something dry and boring like a Dr. Faith zine. Do a load of laundry, empty the dishwasher, something like that. When you feel sleepy again, go back to bed.

Track Your Sleep

For about five minutes, everyone and their dog was wearing a FitBit, smartwatch, or other tracking device. If you still do so, use it to track your sleep! If you don't have one (or, like me, don't want the continuous shaming about your level of inactivity) you can use a sleep tracking app instead. I've been using the SleepCycle app for about two years now, and it's been really helpful. It uses the mic on my phone to track my stages of sleep and quality of sleep. It also listens for distressed breathing and will record a small clip if you are snoring or somesuch. It's caught me having an asthma attack in the middle of the night, which was very needful information. If you notice chronic breathing problems, you could have sleep apnea and you need to get a sleep study to find out.

I recommend this app regularly to people to help us figure out what's going on with their particular sleep situation, because it's waaaay cheaper than another tracking device. Free for thirty days then two bucks a year to use it. (And, in case you are wondering, this is not a paid endorsement. But if the company that made the app wants to support my world tour, I'm good with that.)

Maintain Your General Health

A lot of sleep disruption is due to stomach upset, needing to use the bathroom more, and breathing issues. Using other sleep hacks without treating the root causes may help a bit, but in the long term is more like changing deck chairs on the Titanic than anything else. For example, if you have blood sugar stress, you will likely be up peeing in the middle of the night a lot more than you would otherwise. I'm gonna tattle on Mr. Intimacy Dr. by pointing out how much better he sleeps after he got his blood sugar under control.

Look not just to pharmaceuticals, but also dietary changes, lifestyle changes, and supplements that help manage these issues. A detox diet like Whole30 has you eliminate all common food allergens for thirty days and add them back in, one at a time, every few days while paying attention to your body's reactions. It's a free way of figuring out what food sensitivities might be impacting your health and your sleep. Anytime we can give our body what it needs to heal itself instead of treating symptoms, the better everything works.

Cold it Up

Your body temp needs to drop two to three degrees Fahrenheit (one degree Celsius for anyone on the planet not in the US) in order to be able to sleep. Sleeping in a colder room can really help. Optimally, the room should be about 65 degrees. Most people keep their rooms warmer than that, so 65 may be a big change. Try dropping the thermostat a couple of degrees from where you usually keep it and see if that helps. You can also take a hot bath, since you will have a temperature drop when you get out of the warm water into the cooler air. And while exercise is helpful for sleep in general, exercising close to bedtime will raise your core body temperature and may disrupt your sleep.

No Drankin'

A study just published in the medical journal *Lancet* determined that any health benefits of alcohol (like the classic *"red wine is good for your heart!"*) are far outweighed by the risks. Essentially, the study authors found, there is no such thing as a safe amount, and it is the *leading* risk factor for death and disability adjusted life years for those of us ages 15 to 49. Give it up for a month and track your sleep. If you aren't sure there is an improvement, add it back in and notice the difference, just like you would a food detox. Drinking makes you have to get up and pee more (because it's a diuretic) and it over relaxes your muscles, even in your throat, making it more likely that you will snore. It disrupts your circadian rhythm; it amps up your alpha brain waves, which then compete with your delta brain waves, making the restorative sleep less effective. And it blocks REM sleep like a motherfucker. So seriously. No drankin.' Or at least reduce your amount of alcohol way down. You're tracking your sleep now, so look at the differences on drinking and non-drinking nights.

Avoid Caffeine and Nicotine before Bedtime

Both are stimulants, right? We all have different rates of metabolism for these substances, so pay attention to when you use either and how they affect your sleep. Some people can have coffee after dinner and be fine, some of us need to cut out caffeine after mid-afternoon.

Don't Take Late Naps

Naps in the early afternoon tend to be beneficial to us. Naps later in the afternoon or evening (I know a lot of after-work nappers) can disrupt your nighttime sleep.

I Don't Really Need to Tell You that Sleep Medicines are a Bad Fucking Idea, Do I?

I f sleeping pills induced a natural sleep—meaning, appropriate cycling through NREM and REM sleep—that would be awesome. But they don't. According to studies, sleeping pills (Ambien, Lunesta, and the like) only demonstrate a small improvement in the time it takes to actually fall asleep, and they don't create the brainwaves that we see in real sleep. And they have a fuck-ton of side effects. You've probably heard about people doing crazy zombie shit on sleeping pills. There's also the grogginess and forgetfulness that happens the next day. They are also associated with higher rates of infection and higher rates of cancer. Also? Higher rates of death. All the things that are more likely to happen because of lack of sleep also happen on sleep induced by prescription sleep meds.

The Obligatory Disclaimer about Supplements

I am about to talk about supplements and other options for sleep hygiene. It is super important to discuss these things with your treatment provider before embarking on any of them. I have a postdoc in clinical nutrition, but if I have a client on prescription meds I always talk to their prescriber before adding anything else. Interactions are no joke, and it's important to be careful. Anything you take can also be of concern if you are pregnant, if you are drinking, or if you are using drugs or even over-the-counter medications. A prime example? I went to a tea-making class last year and the person teaching it, a very skilled herbalist, discussed a calming blend that contained St. John's Wort. She failed to mention that St. John's Wort can interact badly with antidepressant medications and HIV medications.

You also need to consider the following statement to hold true to everything I'm discussing in terms of supplemental treatments:

"This statement has not been evaluated by the Food and Drug Administration. This product is not intended to

diagnose, treat, cure, or prevent any disease."

The FDA does not review claims related to structure and function of supplements, which is what we are discussing here. I'm going to discuss the structure of different supplements and what research is out there regarding how they function to help the human body gain equilibrium. And that's not the same as a treatment, right? We are all smart cookies and we got that. I've cited my ass off in terms of the studies related to structure and function, but also encourage you to do your own reading and thinking and talking to your treatment peeps before you start mixing the red and blue pills.

Melatonin and Tryptophan

For every person I've met who has tried melatonin and thought it was brilliant, I've talked to someone else who said it did nothing for them. There's a good reason for that. Our body produces the hormone melatonin in the pineal gland. We generally have enough of it unless we are deficient in some way (as caused by the blue light usage, for example, which is everyone and their dog at this point. More on

managing blue light in a minute). Melatonin
works best if you take it 2-3 *hours* before you
go to bed, since it helps amp up the body's
own natural melatonin kicking -n as part of
your circadian cycle. If you take it like you
would a sleeping pill (swallow pill and lie
down) you'll not get near the same effect.

Even if you are taking it exactly when you are
supposed to, you may notice that you fall asleep
pretty well, but the *staying* asleep portion of
the program is still problematic. You're not
the only one. Most melatonin supplements are
fast acting instead of continued release, so
you get your little burst but then it wears
off.

One of the other supplements I often suggest
is L-Tryptophan (yes, the stuff in turkey).
It is one of the essential amino acids that
the body doesn't produce on its own (unlike
melatonin). We have to get it from our foods
or in supplementation. L-Tryptophan is used
by the body to make niacin. Niacin makes,
among other things, serotonin. And serotonin
is instrumental in our melatonin production.

Now I know you're thinking, "Wait, what?
Serotonin? Does that make L-Tryptophan an
antidepressant?" Some research shows that
L-Tryptophan does demonstrate some relief of

depression-related symptoms. If you are able to add it in, you may be able to talk to your prescriber about reducing or discontinuing other medications you have been taking for depression. But let them in on what you're doing before you start futzing with your dosages, mmmkay?

If you add L-Tryptophan, you may still use a little melatonin to help the falling asleep part, but you won't need nearly the dose because the L-Tryptophan will keep it producing throughout the night like a champ. And, yes, there are multiple studies that demonstrate L-Tryptophan supplementation works like a boss for promoting sleep.

Cannabis and Kratom? Danger, Will Robinson!

The research on both is limited, I realize. Most cannabis and sleep research comes from the 70s, though with it being legal in more states, we will see better studies and confirmatory studies over the next few years. Kratom (the tropical tree leaf that has stimulant and opioid properties) is legal in most states but new to the U.S. in general, so also has limited studies to back it up.

I know that a lot of people use cannabis (CBD or THC) or kratom to help them manage their symptoms of anxiety, depression, PTSD, and chronic pain. However, the research that *is* out there does show that both disrupt sleep quality, specifically by reducing REM sleep (which we now know is kinda sorta really fucking important). Sleep problems on kratom is an oft-reported side effect. With cannabis, it's slightly more complicated. Deep sleep is enhanced with initial use, but the cannabis-helping-you-sleep effect fades away pretty quickly the more you use it. Since research is fairly limited, the "why" part of that is still unknown.

Because cannabis disrupts REM sleep, it also lessens night terrors, and is used by folks with PTSD and the like. But then you also lose all the things REM sleep gives the human body, so not a good trade-off. There is a prescription option that may work better. Many individuals with PTSD have higher levels of norepinephrine (noradrenaline) released by the nervous system. Meaning that the hormone/ neurotransmitter that the body uses to engage the fight-or-flight response is swimming around in their heads, promoting alertness, even when they are supposed to be sleeping. Makes sense that noradrenaline release seems associated with night terrors. Some docs are using a high blood pressure drug called Prazosin, which has the side benefit of suppressing the noradrenaline without suppressing REM sleep. Something to chat with your prescriber about if this is something you struggle with.

For those of you who are using cannabis and/or kratom to help you manage other symptoms, I feel you. I know many people consider them an absolute lifesaver. The lesser the dose, the less impact it has on your sleep. Monitor your dosing along with monitoring your sleep, and work to figure out your sweet spot on amount you take and time(s) of day you take it to find your best balance.

And if you smoke your THC? Consider using another method of ingestion. Smoking increases your risk of breathing issues (asthma, COPSD), which will also fuck with your sleep.

Get the TV Out of the Bedroom

Bedrooms are for two things, and watching TV isn't one of them. It's bad for your partnership and it's really fucking bad for your sleep. A poll taken by a TV manufacturer (LG, to be precise) found that 61% of people fall asleep with the TV on. Besides the blue light disruption, the cacophonous noise in the background is going to disrupt your sleep quality. If you do better with noise at night, try a noise machine. Many of them offer different settings from white noise, like rain or heartbeats. A lot of people also use a fan or air purifier. Both make white noise while helping with air circulation and cleaning toxins out of your space.

Sun Exposure and Blue Blockers

Try to get natural sun exposure during the day and limit your blue light exposure in the evenings. Charles Czeisler of Harvard Medical School found that individuals who used electronic reading devices (like Kindles) before bedtime had a harder time falling asleep, had reduced levels of melatonin in the body, and were groggier the next morning. Like a 50% reduction in melatonin levels. That's a big deal.

It's the blue light coming from our screens, y'all. Whether it's an e-reader, our phones, or the TV, our constant exposure to blue light confuses our brain into thinking it's daytime for longer than it actually is.

27

And if you're *thinking "Fuck off, Dr. Faith. Watching Netflix in bed is my low-key reason for living. I'm not giving that up"?* Studies have demonstrated that people who used blue light devices and wore blue blocker glasses for three hours before bedtime produced just as much melatonin as people who were not exposed to blue lights. And the glasses are super-inexpensive. A pair that is obviously yellow and look like what Bono wears is about ten bucks. If you want a pair that does the trick without being so overtly weird, you can get them for twenty or so bucks. They are still yellow tinted to block the blue light, but it isn't obvious up close. You can also get them in different reading glass strengths. I think they're actually kinda cute. See my pair?

Another option is to download a program like f.lux on your computer. It will change your computer display's light settings to match what the sun is doing outside. I'm currently typing on my laptop at 8PM and the light is a dimmer pink, so I don't need to wear my blue blockers of sassiness.

Weighted Blankets are like a Sleep Hug

Weighted blankets are superb for supporting individuals who live with anxiety, ADHD, ASD, and other issues. They have also been shown to support sleep. Weighted blankets provide deep touch pressure, which raises serotonin levels in the body which, as we know from above, promotes the generation and release of melatonin in the body. Weighted blankets used to be prohibitively expensive, but now can be found for under 100 dollars with some research. For adults, you generally want to get a weight that is 5-10% of your ideal body weight. For kiddos, the general number is 10% of their body weight plus a pound of two.

Other weighting options can include "Korean mink" blankets (which I've seen available for up to 10 pounds for about 30 dollars, and no-they are not actually real mink) or just piling on whatever blankets you have in the house. If you do the pile-on trick, you will probably have to drop the temperature in the house some more because it will be significantly warmer. Weighted blankets use plastic pellets for the weight, and therefore aren't as hot to have over the body.

Valerian and Kava

The valerian root and kava plant have both been used for their sedative effects for thousands of years, and can therefore be beneficial for sleep. While I'm a fan of both, I am more cautious about the brands being used than I am with melatonin and L-Tryptophan. Both of these supplements are more expensive to produce, making it more likely that you end up buying something with a non-efficacious dose because the manufacturer is trying to amp their bottom line.

I prefer the Mediherb brand because the quality is above and beyond, and the manufacturing is so transparent. Annnnnnd because they water-extract their kava in order to eliminate many of the side effects associated with other extract processes. If you've heard about kava being unsafe, you were reading about kava lactone toxicity. Essentially, some extraction methods used on the kava plant also extract glutathione, which can damage the liver. Clearly no bueno. Mediherb products are only available through professional treatment providers. For over-the-counter brands that are good quality, I lean toward Gaia Herbs and Mountain Rose Herbs. You may also find an herbalist in your area that makes their own extractions so you can see their process up close and personal.

Chamomile Tea

Yes, Grandma was right to give you chamomile. It's generally really safe, per the FDA. Though if you have a ragweed allergy, you may react to chamomile. They are from the same fam.

You do need to make sure you brew it properly. Use two to three tea bags and put a cover over the pot or your cup so all of the good oils don't escape in the steam. Drinky-drinky for a relaxing effect.

Banana Peel Tea

Banana peels are not just brilliant in your compost pile (or fed directly to your rose bushes), you can make an amazing tea out of them. Cut off the stems and use them fresh, baggy and freeze them to use frozen, or dehydrate them to use later. One fresh peel is equal to about two tablespoons of dried peel, all of which is equal to one cup of tea. Boil water, throw in the peel, then cover and reduce heat to let it simmer for about ten minutes. You can add cinnamon and vanilla if you dig, as well. Bananas (including the peels) are a good source of magnesium and potassium—both things our bodies need anyway, and something many people tend to not have enough of. Bananas also contain L-Tryptophan, so *boom.*

Cognitive Behavior Therapy for Insomnia (CBT-I)

The Chronic Insomnia Task Force of the American Academy of Sleep Medicine has recommended CBT-I as the first professional intervention that someone should undertake for insomnia (assuming apnea, restless leg syndrome, and other medical conditions have been ruled out). CBT-I is a short-term therapy (four to eight sessions, generally) that pairs the principles of cognitive behavior therapy with specific sleep hygiene protocols and relaxation techniques to assist people in untethering the emotional distress that is the general root cause of insomnia to begin with.

If you are disrupted consistently by nightmares and night terrors, that means your brain is working hard to make sense of some traumatic shit you have dealt with in the past. CBT-I may be enough to help you through the process, or you may have to do some trauma-informed therapy to work through whatever it is that your brain is trying to make sense of.

Conclusion

I used to be a typical American dumbass about sleep. The first semester of my doctoral program is when I truly scared myself. I had been studying for my stats class at Panera Bread with my cohort, when on my way out of the parking lot I drove directly into a concrete lamppost.

I was going all of four miles an hour in an empty shopping center. The concrete post didn't even jump out in front of me (you know, the way a *living being* would). I wasn't on my phone, playing music, or talking to anyone in the passenger seat. I had no distractions except my own exhaustion. I literally just didn't see it until I hit it.

I am so grateful that's the only thing that happened, and it scared me into becoming the sleep queen. And if you are reading this, I know you have a similar investment. Sleep is even more important than food and movement. And those of us making these changes start challenging the larger bullshit culture that thinks we can out-think our most elemental recovery tool.

Now go back to bed.

References

Admin. "Understanding CBD: The Calming and Sleep Promoting Benefits of Cannabidiol." *Your Guide to Better Sleep*, Your Guide to Better Sleep, 29 Jan. 2018, TheSleepDoctor.com/2017/08/10/understanding-cbd/

Alison, et al. "How To Make Banana Tea For Restful Sleep." *Mommypotamus*, 30 July 2018, www.mommypotamus.com/banana-tea-for-sleep/.

Bloomberg.com, Bloomberg, www.bloomberg.com/news/articles/2018-08-23/no-amount-of-alcohol-use-is-safe-analysis-of-studies-finds.

Burkhart, K, and J R Phelps. "Amber Lenses to Block Blue Light and Improve Sleep: a Randomized Trial." *Advances in Pediatrics.*, U.S. National Library of Medicine, Dec. 2009, www.ncbi.nlm.nih.gov/pubmed/20030543.

Buysse DJ. Sleep health: can we define it? Does it matter? *SLEEP* 2014;37(1):9-17.

"Cannabis and Sleep." *Psychology Today*, Sussex Publishers, www.psychologytoday.com/us/blog/sleepless-in-america/201211/cannabis-and-sleep.

"Cannabis as a Sleep Aid: Here's What You Need to Know." *Healthline*, Healthline Media, www.healthline.com/health/medical-marijuana/cannabis-for-sleeping precautions.

"Circadian Rhythm." *Psychology Today*, Sussex Publishers, www.psychologytoday.com/us/basics/circadian-rhythm.

Czeisler, Charles A. "Perspective: Casting Light on Sleep Deficiency." *Nature News*, Nature Publishing Group, 22 May 2013, www.nature.com/articles/497S13a.

Davis, Jeanie Lerche. "Sleep Supplements: Melatonin, Valerian, and More." *WebMD*, WebMD, www.webmd.com/diet/features/natural-good-sleep-tips-on-melatonin-valerian 1.

Figueiro, M G, et al. "The Impact of Light from Computer Monitors on Melatonin Levels in College Students." *Advances in Pediatrics.*, U.S. National Library of Medicine, www.ncbi.nlm.nih.gov/pubmed/21552190.

Gallagher, James. "Sleep Cleans the Brain of Toxins-BBC News." BBC, BBC, 17 Oct. 2013, www.bbc.co.uk/news/health-24567412.

Ghosh, Pallab. "Why Do We Sleep?" BBC News, BBC, 15 May 2015, www.bbc.com/news/science-environment-32606341.

Gillette, M U, and S A Tischkau. "Suprachiasmatic Nucleus: the Brain's Circadian Clock." *Advances in Pediatrics.*, U.S. National Library of Medicine, www.ncbi.nlm.nih.gov/pubmed/10548871.

Gooley, Joshua J., et al. *Advances in Pediatrics.*, U.S. National Library of Medicine, Mar. 2011, www.ncbi.nlm.nih.gov/pmc/articles/PMC3047226/.

Hartmann, E. "Effects of L-Tryptophan on Sleepiness and on Sleep." *Advances in Pediatrics.*, U.S. National Library of Medicine, www.ncbi.nlm.nih.gov/pubmed/6764927/.

"How Alcohol Affects the Quality-And Quantity-Of Sleep." *National Sleep Foundation*, sleepfoundation.org/sleep-topics/how-alcohol-affects-sleep.

"How Blocking Blue Light at Night Can Transform Your Sleep." *Healthline*, Healthline Media, www.healthline.com/nutrition/block-blue-light-to-sleep-better section2.

"Kava Lactones and the Kava-Kava Controversy." *Egyptian Journal of Medical Human Genetics*, Elsevier, 29 Aug. 2003, www.sciencedirect.com/science/article/abs/pii/S0031942203003819.

"Kratom: Is It Safe?" *Healthline*, Healthline Media, www.healthline.com/health/food-nutrition/is-kratom-safe side-effects.

Mandal, Ananya. "What Is Adenosine?" *News-Medical.net,* News-Medical.net, 23 Aug. 2018, www.news-medical.net/health/What-is-Adenosine.aspx.

"Melatonin: How It Affects Sleep—Watch WebMD Video." *WebMD*, WebMD, www.webmd.com/sleep-disorders/video/melatonin-sleep.

Peters, Brandon. "How Does Adenosine Help You Get a Good Night's Sleep?" Verywell Health, Verywellhealth, www.verywellhealth.com/adenosine-and-sleep-3015337.

Purves, Dale. "Neuroglial Cells." *Advances in Pediatrics.*, U.S. National Library of Medicine, 1 Jan. 1970, www.ncbi.nlm.nih.gov/books/NBK10869/.

Shaw, K, et al. "Tryptophan and 5-Hydroxytryptophan for Depression." *Advances in Pediatrics.*, U.S. National Library of Medicine, www.ncbi.nlm.nih.gov/pubmed/11869656.

Singh, D, et al. "Severity of Pain and Sleep Problems during Kratom (Mitragyna Speciosa Korth.) Cessation among Regular Kratom Users." *Advances in Pediatrics.*, U.S. National Library of Medicine, www.ncbi.nlm.nih.gov/pubmed/29558272/.

"Touch for Socioemotional and Physical Well-Being: A Review." *Egyptian Journal of Medical Human Genetics*, Elsevier, 25 Feb. 2011, www.sciencedirect.com/science/article/pii/S0273229711000025.

Walker, Matthew P. *Why We Sleep: Unlocking the Power of Sleep and Dreams*. Scribner, an Imprint of Simon & Schuster, Inc., 2018.

"What Falling Asleep With the TV On Is Really Doing to Your Health." *Health.com*, www.health.com/sleep/falling-asleep-tv-on.

"What Is Melatonin?" *WebMD*, WebMD, www.webmd.com/sleep-disorders/what-is-melatonin.

"What Is Sleep? Why Is It Needed?-American Sleep Association." *American Sleep Assoc*, American Sleep Association, www.sleepassociation.org/about-sleep/what-is-sleep/.

"Why Do We Sleep, Anyway?" *Sleep and Memory | Need Sleep*, healthysleep.med.harvard.edu/healthy/matters/benefits-of-sleep/why-do-we-sleep.

Zamosky, Lisa. "The Truth About Tryptophan." *WebMD*, WebMD, www.webmd.com/food-recipes/features/the-truth-about-tryptophan 1.